A Visit To The Farm

Written by Mark S. Bernthal • Photography by Dennis Full

It is a beautiful morning on the farm! The sun is rising and the cockerel crows, "Cock-a-doodle-dooooo!"

Barney jumps for joy, shouting,
"Another day of fun on the
farm! Boy, oh boy!"

"I love playing on the farm,"
says Baby Bop.
"But we have to work today,
Sis," BJ reminds her.

"That's right," says Barney. "Farmers must start work early because they have so many jobs to do. Let's go and see some of the animals."

In the stable, BJ feeds hay to Copper, the horse.
"Here's your breakfast," says BJ.

Copper munches happily on the hay.

Barney has milked Clara the cow. She mooooos happily.

Baby Bop does a chicken dance and cackles, "Cluck-cluck, cluck-cluck!"

Barney has driven the big tractor to the corn field.

"Varooooom, vroooom," says Baby Bop. "I like the red tractor, Barney!"

Barney and BJ pick corn in the summer sunshine. "Whew! I'm hot!" says BJ, mopping his forehead.

Baby Bop pops her
head around a stalk of
corn and giggles,
"Peek-a-boo, you two!"

Barney and BJ herd the cattle into the field. The cows and their calves can eat a delicious lunch of fresh green grass.

Baby Bop is ringing a cowbell. "Come on everyone, follow me!" she calls.

Barney and BJ pick lots of vegetables. They fill their baskets with tomatoes, beans, carrots and one of Barney's favourite vegetables – a purple aubergine!

Baby Bop watches them work. "This marrow makes a good seat!" she laughs.

Barney, Baby Bop and BJ carry baskets of vegetables back to the farm.

"We won't have to go shopping for supper today," says Baby Bop. "That's right," says Barney. "We have all we need right here."

After supper, Baby Bop falls fast asleep. "BJ, I think Baby Bop played as hard as we worked today," says Barney with a chuckle.

1. What sound does the Cockerel make?
   (a) baa-aa   (b) moo-oo
   (c) cock-a-doodle -dooooo

2. What sound does a horse make?

3. What sound does a sheep make?

4. Match the following to tell us what each animal gives us:
   - Goat
   - Hen
   - Sheep
   - Wool
   - Milk
   - Eggs